THE ART OF MINDFULNESS

SERENE AND TRANQUIL COLOURING

 Michael O'Mara Books Limited

First published in Great Britain in 2015 by
Michael O'Mara Books Limited
9 Lion Yard
Tremadoc Road
London SW4 7NQ

A CIP catalogue record for this book is available from the British Library.

Papers used by Michael O'Mara Books Limited are natural, recyclable products
made from wood grown in sustainable forests. The manufacturing processes
conform to the environmental regulations of the country of origin.

ISBN: 978-1-78243-494-8

3 4 5 6 7 8 9 10

www.mombooks.com

Designed by Ana Bjezancevic and Claire Cater

Illustrations by Amanda Hillier, Andrew Rowland, Chellie Carroll, Claire Cater,
Jake McDonald, Jo Taylor, Julie Ingham, Louise Wright, Michelle Breen,
Sam Loman and Sherise Seven Art

Cover illustration by Angelea Van Dam

Printed and bound in Malta

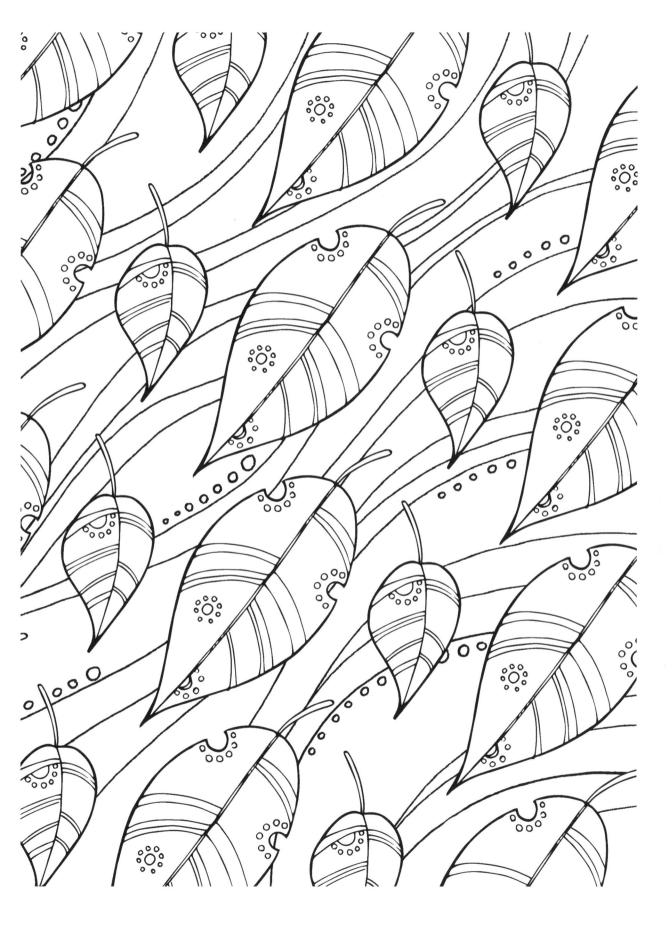

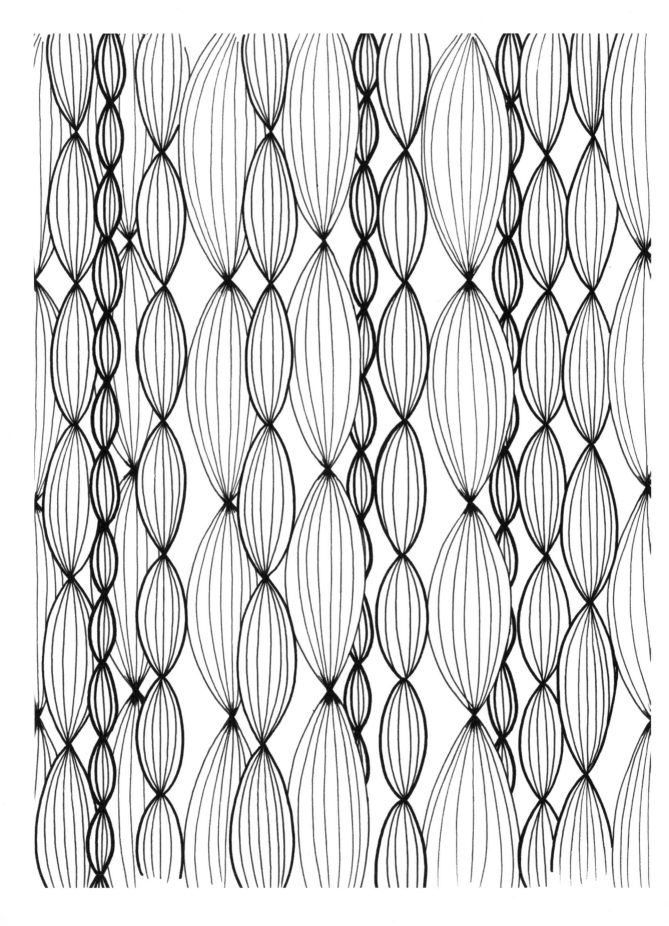

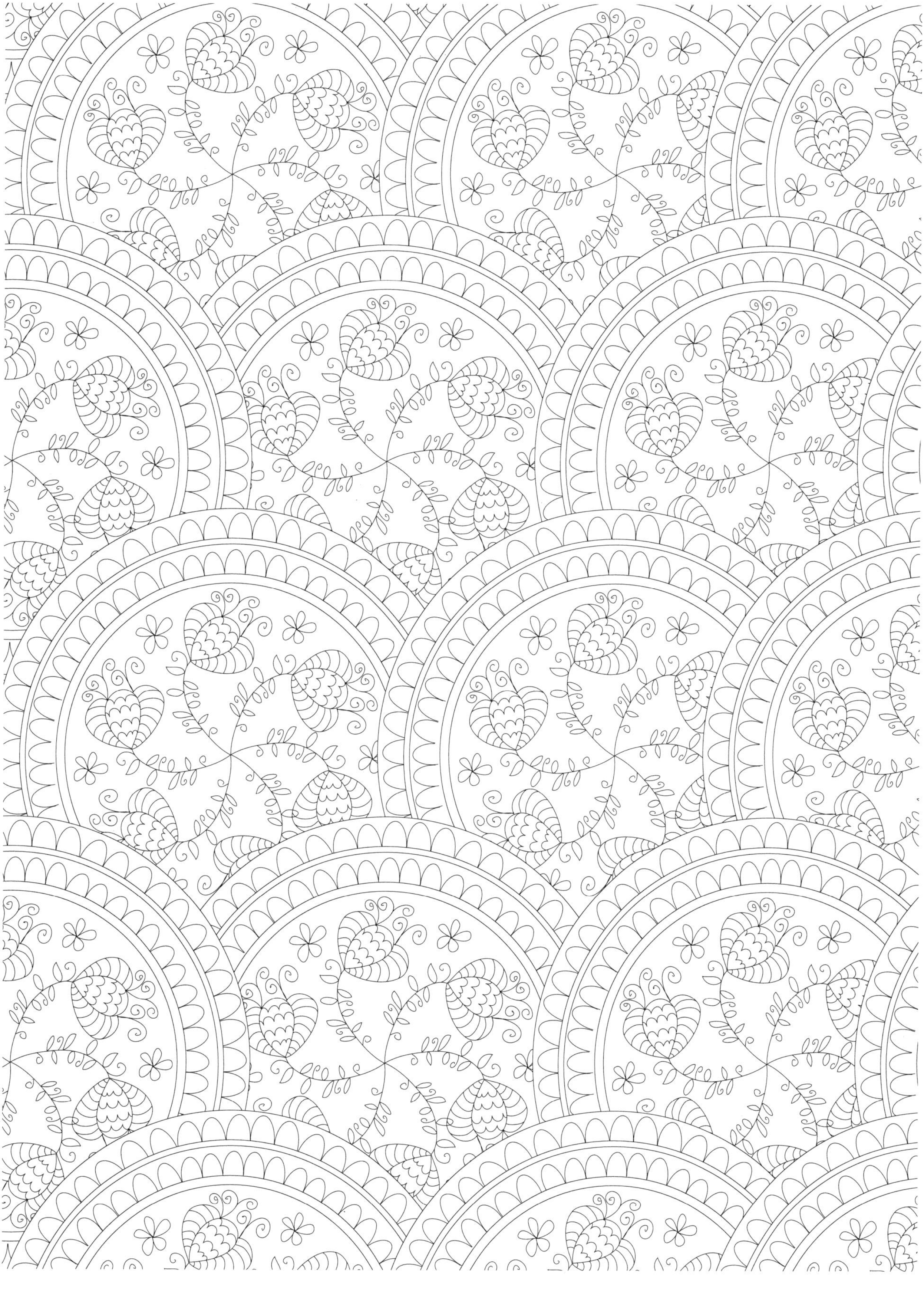